Holy Pascha Week
Coloring Book for Children

Written by
Yostina Youssef

Illustrated by
Mina Anton

Holy Pascha Week
Coloring Book for Children

© 2019 by ACTS Press

ac✛s
P·R·E·S·S

www.acts.press

Paperback
978-1-940661-14-8

Saddle Stitch
978-1-940661-22-3

Printed in the United States of America

A Word from the Editor

'Therefore, children, let us hold fast to the practice of asceticism and not grow careless. For, in this, we have the Lord working with us, as it is written: "To all that choose the good, the Lord works with them for good" (Ro 8:28).[1]

With great joy, we present to our beloved parents and children this Coptic Orthodox coloring book for children published by ACTS Press under the auspices of His Eminence Metropolitan Serapion and the guidance of His Grace Bishop Kyrillos, Auxiliary Bishop for Christian Education in the Diocese of Los Angeles, Southern California, and Hawaii.

The goal of Orthodox Christianity is to unite every aspect of person's life with Christ. Nowhere is this more evident than with our children. We baptize them shortly after birth and immediately unite them with Christ through the life of the Church and participation in the Holy Mysteries. We feed their minds with the inspired words of Holy Scripture and teach them to sanctify their bodies through fasting and purity.

This coloring book is presented as a wholesome activity to help parents and children journey through the Holy Pascha Week, commemorating the life-giving work of our Lord Jesus Christ for our salvation. With simple language and engaging illustrations, children are encouraged to meditate on our Lord's Passion and life-giving sacrifice, which ultimately will lead them closer to Christ Himself. Not only will children benefit, but also parents who complete this beautiful activity with their children, for parents are the first models of holiness for their children. When children see their parents reflecting the love, patience, and holiness of our Lord Jesus Christ and His saints, they necessarily imitate them.

For this reason, we encourage parents and children alike to contemplate the events of the Holy Pascha Week and color these pages with faith and love as they both grow in their relationship with God and with one another.

The Editor

---

1   St. Athanasius, *"Life of St. Anthony," in Early Christian Biographies*, ed. Hermigild Dressler and Roy J. Deferrari, trans. Mary Emily Keenan, vol. 15, The Fathers of the Church (Washington, DC: The Catholic University of America Press, 1952), 152.

Ϧⲉⲛ ⲫⲣⲁⲛ ⲙ̀Ⲫⲓⲱⲧ ⲛⲉⲙ Ⲡ̀ϣⲏⲣⲓ ⲛⲉⲙ Ⲡⲓⲡ̀ⲛⲉⲩⲙⲁ ⲉⲑⲟⲩⲁⲃ. Ⲟⲩⲛⲟⲩϯ ⲛ̀ⲟⲩⲱⲧ. Ⲁⲙⲏⲛ.

In the Name of the Father, the Son, and the Holy Spirit.

One God. Amen.

Holy Pascha Week or Holy Week is the week that we follow our Lord Jesus Christ, step by step on His journey to the Cross for our salvation. Our Lord and Savior, Jesus Christ, dies on the Cross to save us from our sins because of His great, enormous, gigantic love for us!

On Lazarus Saturday, Jesus raises His friend from the dead. Lazarus had been dead for four days, but nothing is impossible for God. Jesus says, "I am the Resurrection and the Life" (Jn 11:25).

That night, Jesus was having dinner at Lazarus' house with Lazarus and his sisters, Mary and Martha. Mary anointed Christ's feet with expensive perfume and wiped them with her hair. Jesus told us that she did this to prepare for His burial.

Early Sunday morning, Jesus was walking through Jericho, when a crowd gathered. A tax collector named Zacchaeus couldn't see Jesus because he was so short. He wanted to see Jesus so much that he climbed a large sycamore tree. The Lord rewarded his determination by visiting his home. Zacchaeus said sorry to everyone he did wrong to and paid back everything he took from them.

On Palm Sunday, Jesus rides a donkey into Jerusalem. Our Lord is the King of Kings, but He entered Jerusalem in a humble way. The people spread palm branches and coats on the road before Him and shout, "Hosanna to the Son of David!" So, we decorate the Church and carry palm branches every Palm Sunday.

That night, our Lord teaches His disciples the importance of faith. He tells them that even if their faith is as small as a tiny mustard seed, they can tell a mountain to move from here to there and it will!

When fig trees are covered in leaves, that means there are fruit on the tree. But on Monday, Jesus passed a fig tree that had leaves without any fruit. He told the tree that it would never feed a person again, and it didn't! Jesus does this to remind us of the power of our faith and also to encourage us to have fruit in our lives, like listening to our parents and being kind to others.

On Tuesday, Jesus tells us a parable. A "parable" is a made-up story that has an important lesson. This parable is about a business man who gives three workers different amounts of money. Two of them use it carefully to earn more. But the third one is not smart and just buries it. When the business man comes back, he rewards the first two workers, but the third is punished for wasting his chance. We pray to be like the first two and use God's gifts to do good things.

On Tuesday night, Jesus tells us another parable, this one is about ten virgins going to a wedding. While the virgins get ready, five are smart and bring oil to light their lamps. But the other five are not smart and bring their lamps with no oil. It gets late and dark, the smart virgins light their lamps using their oil, but the virgins who have no oil need to go buy some and miss the wedding. Jesus is teaching us to always be ready with good deeds and choices that will be a light in our lives.

On Wednesday, we see two people treat Jesus very differently. One of His disciples, Judas Iscariot, betrays Jesus for thirty pieces of silver. To betray is to break a friendship or a promise. But another person, shows us how we should be with Jesus. A woman anoints Jesus' feet with perfume, when He is at the home of Simon in Bethany. She shows kindness and love to our Lord. We can anoint Jesus too, with kindness and love to our family and friends.

On Thursday, Jesus shares His Holy Body and Precious Blood with His disciples and teaches us to continue this Holy Mystery. He also washes the feet of each of His disciples to show them the importance of serving others.

That night, Jesus prays in the Garden of Gethsemane, when Judas brings a troop of soldiers to capture Him. Judas signals the soldiers with a kiss for Jesus. He is arrested and taken to the high priest.

On Friday morning, Jesus is put on trial, even though He did nothing wrong. Bad people tell lies to get Jesus in trouble. Our Lord Jesus Christ explains to Pontius Pilate, "My kingdom is not of this world" (Jn 18:36).

At the Third Hour, at nine o'clock in the morning, Pontius Pilate wants to let Jesus go. But the people shout for Him to be crucified. "Crucified" means to die while being hung on a cross. Pilate washes his hands, meaning he doesn't want any responsibility in this decision and lets the people crucify our Lord.

Around noon, Jesus carries the Cross through the city of Jerusalem to an outer hill called Golgotha. Pontius Pilate writes a sign to put on the Cross that says, "King of the Jews." Our Lord is crucified with two thieves, one on the right and the other on the left.

In the Ninth Hour, at three o'clock in the afternoon, Jesus uses the first line of Psalm 21 to remind the people that His crucifixion was prophesied many years ago. A "prophecy" is a saying that tells what is going to happen in the future. Jesus says, "Eli, Eli, lama sabachthani?" that is, "My God, My God, why have You forsaken Me?" (Mt 27:46).

In the Eleventh Hour, at five o'clock in the evening, Jesus died on the Cross and there was a huge earthquake and the veil in the Temple tore in two. The veil was a curtain that separated God's place in the Temple from the people's area. God allowed for the veil to tear in two to show Jesus' triumph over death, there is no more separation between God and people.

ⲠⲈⲔⲐⲢⲞⲚⲞⲤ ⲪϮ ϢⲀ ⲈⲚⲈϨ Ⲛ̄ⲦⲈ ⲠⲒⲈⲚⲈϨ

In the Twelfth Hour, at sunset, Jesus is buried in a tomb with the help of His friends, Joseph of Arimathaea and Nicodemus. We sing a beautiful verse from Psalm 44:6, "Your throne, O God, is forever and ever; a scepter of righteousness is the scepter of Your kingdom." This verse reminds us that this earth is only for a short while and that Heaven is our forever home with Jesus.

Friday night through Saturday morning is a special time in the Church called "Apocalypse" or "Bright" or "Joyful" Saturday. All the hymns and readings from the Bible are focused on Heaven and how we will live there. On this night the Church is decorated for the Resurrection, with white and gold banners to show our joy that Heaven is open for us because of our Lord Jesus Christ.

Finally, the Resurrection is celebrated very early on Sunday morning! Jesus is alive again and shows Himself to His disciples. That day, two of His apostles were walking to a village called Emmaus. Jesus appeared to them, but they couldn't recognize Him. Our Lord and Savior explained all the prophesies to them and how He fulfilled them with the Cross and the Resurrection.

Made in the USA
Coppell, TX
07 April 2022

76158580R00020